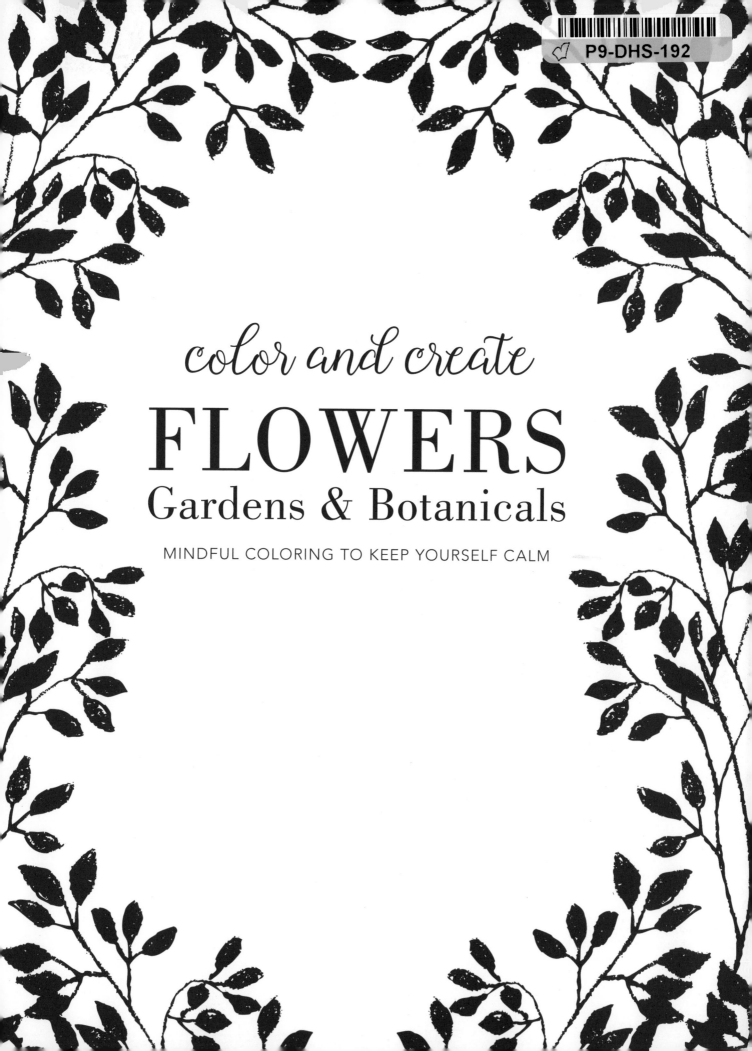

color and create

FLOWERS

Gardens & Botanicals

MINDFUL COLORING TO KEEP YOURSELF CALM

METRO BOOKS
New York

An imprint of Sterling Publishing
1166 Avenue of the Americas
New York, NY 10036

METRO BOOKS and the distinctive Metro Books logo are trademarks of Sterling Publishing Co., Inc.

Copyright © 2015 by Octopus Publishing Group

ISBN 978-1-4351-6201-3

For information about custom editions, special sales, and premium and corporate purchases, please contact Sterling Special Sales at 800-805-5489 or specialsales@sterlingpublishing.com.

Acknowledgements:
Publisher: Samantha Warrington
Design: Wide Open Studios
Art Director: Miranda Snow
Editor: Phoebe Morgan

Manufactured in China

4 6 8 10 9 7 5 3

www.sterlingpublishing.com

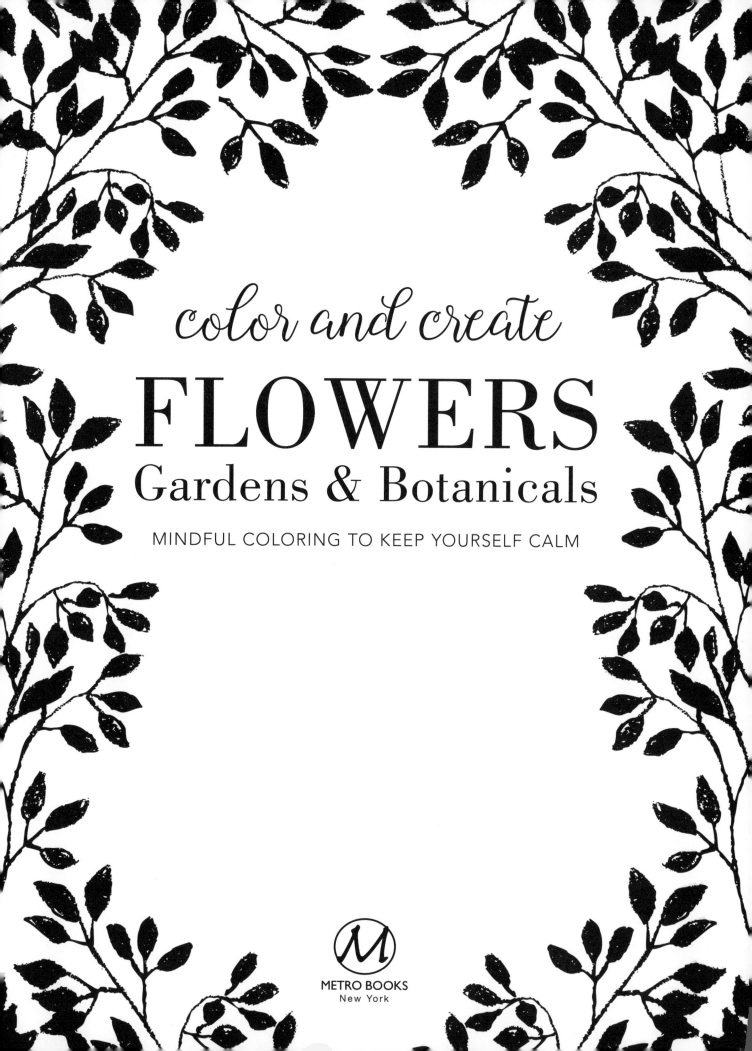

color and create
FLOWERS
Gardens & Botanicals

MINDFUL COLORING TO KEEP YOURSELF CALM

METRO BOOKS
New York

Where flowers bloom, so does hope

Lady Bird Johnson

Always be fragrant

Don't wait for someone to bring
you flowers. Plant your own garden and
decorate your own soul

A life without
dreams is like
a garden without
flowers

To plant a garden is to
believe in tomorrow.

Audrey Hepburn

The earth laughs in flowers

Ralph Waldo Emerson

In search of my mother's garden,
I found my own.

Friends are the flowers in
the garden of life

March winds and April
showers bring forth
Spring flowers

A flower cannot bloom without sunshine,
and man cannot live without love

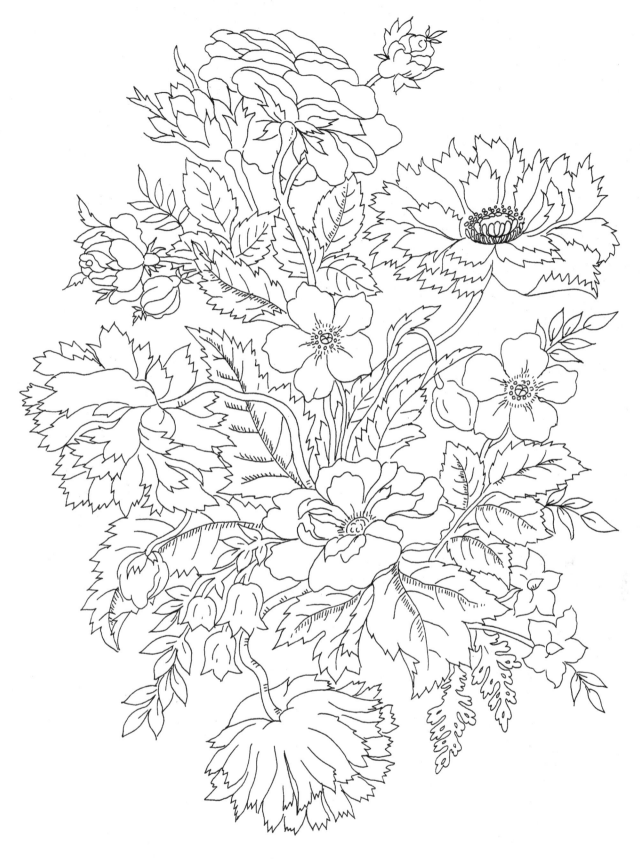

A life with love will have some thorns,
but a life without love will have no roses

Every flower is a
soul blossoming
in nature

Gerard de Nerval

Take time to stop and smell the roses

A rose speaks of love silently, in a language known only to the heart

Just living is not enough.
One must have sunshine,
freedom and a little flower.

Hans Christian Anderson

A single rose can be my garden... a single
friend, my world.

Leo Buscaglia

We can complain because rose bushes
have thorns, or rejoice because thorn
bushes have roses.

Abraham Lincoln

I feel as if I opened a book and found roses of yesterday, sweet and fragrant between its leaves

Lady Bird Johnson

What sunshine is to flowers,
smiles are to humanity

There are always flowers for those who want to see them.

Henri Matisse

Let a hundred flowers bloom.
Mao Zedong

I will soothe you and heal you
I will bring you roses
I too have been covered with thorns
Rumi

Like wildflowers, you must allow yourself
to grow in all the places that people
thought you never would.

E.V.

May flowers bloom in all corners
of your world

Flowers are happy things.

P. G. Wodehouse

Even if I knew that tomorrow the world
would go to pieces, I would still plant my
apple tree

Martin Luther

A flower does not think of competing
with the flower next to it. It just blooms.

Weeds are flowers too, once you get to know them.

A. A. Milne

All the flowers of all the tomorrows are in
the seeds of today

Our Family: Like branches on a tree, we all grow in different directions but we stay strong because we share the same roots

Life is not greener on the other side, it's greener where you tend it

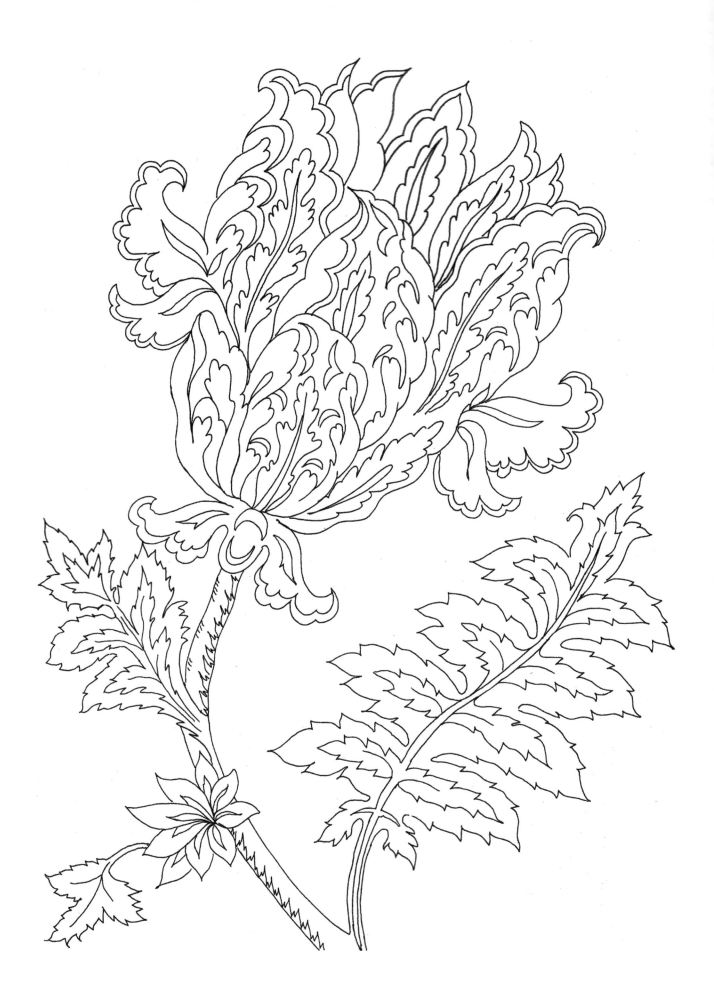

Beauty is a golden
leaf that falls from
an autumn tree

The trees that are slow to grow
bear the best fruit

Moliere

Stretching his hand up to meet the stars,
so often man forgets the flowers at his feet.

Jeremy Bentham

Life is the blossom of
which love is the honey

Treat your relationship like a plant –
pay attention to it and nurture it and it
will blossom

All I need are palm trees and
a little bit of paradise

If you think in terms of a year, plant a seed;
if you think in terms of ten years, plant
a tree; if you thing in terms of 100 years,
teach the people.

Confucius

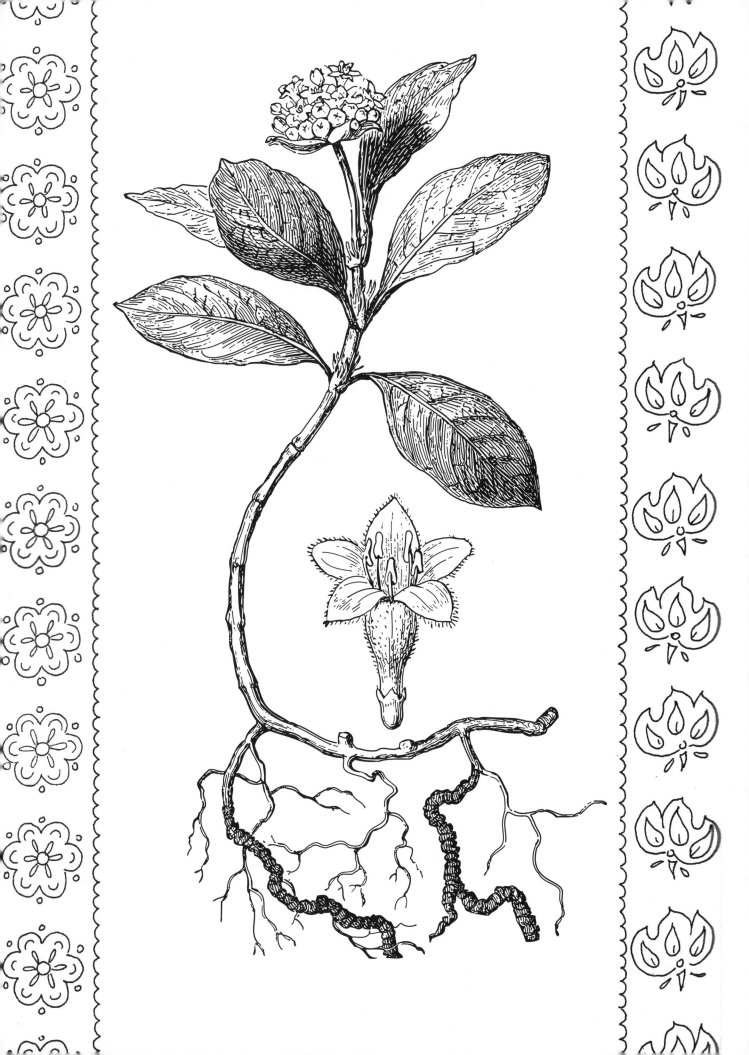

The flower that blooms in adversity is the most rare and beautiful of all.

Mulan

A friend is someone who overlooks
your broken gate and sees the flowers in
your garden

I love my little garden;
it's where I go to find myself when
I get lost in the world

There is always music in the trees, but
your heart must be quiet to hear it

Minnie Aumonier

Flowers can't solve problems but they can
make your eyes smile

If things get dark and difficult,
remember that flowers have to get through
a lot of dirt to find the light

This may not be the Garden of Eden,
but it's my own precious patch of paradise

I'd rather have roses on my
table than diamonds round
my neck.

Emma Goldman

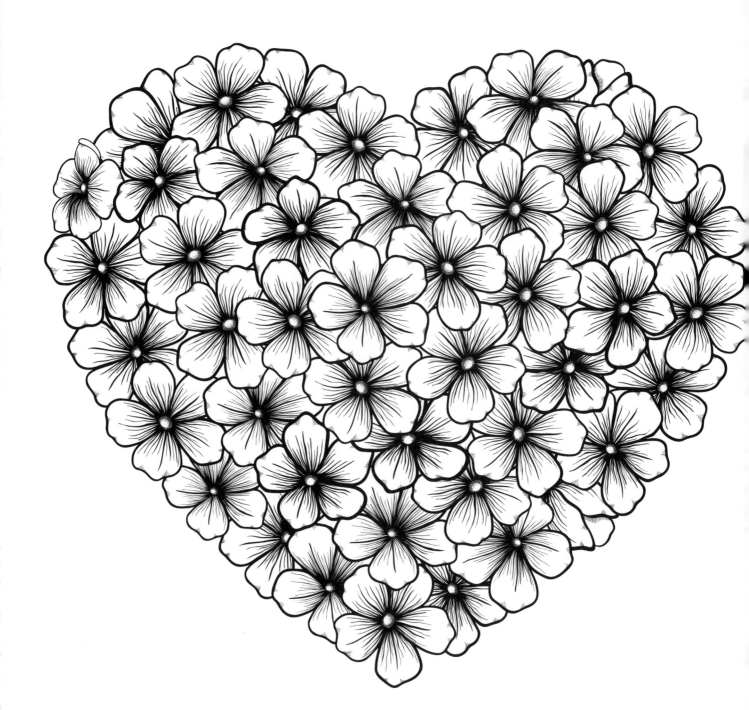

Your mind is the garden;
your ideas are the seeds